THE ROYAL HORTICULTURAL SOCIETY

DIARY 2009

Commentary by Brent Elliott

Illustrations from the
Royal Horticultural Society's
Lindley Library

F

FRANCES LINCOLN LIMITED
PUBLISHERS

Frances Lincoln Limited
4 Torriano Mews
Torriano Avenue
London NW5 2RZ
www.franceslincoln.com

The Royal Horticultural Society Diary 2009
Copyright © Frances Lincoln limited 2008

British Library cataloguing-in-publication data
A catalogue record for this book is available from the British Library

ISBN: 978-0-7112-2959-4

Printed in China
First Frances Lincoln edition 2008

RHS FLOWER SHOWS 2009

All shows feature a wide range of floral exhibits staged by the nursery trade, with
associated competitions reflecting seasonal changes and horticultural sundries.
With the exception of the shows held at Cardiff, Malvern, Chelsea, Hampton Court,
Tatton Park and Wisley, all RHS Flower Shows will be held in one or both of the
Society's Horticultural Halls in Greycoat Street and Vincent Square, Westminster,
London SW1.

The dates given are correct at the time of going to press, but before travelling to a
show, we strongly advise you to check with the Compass section of the RHS journal
The Garden, or telephone the 24-hour Flower Show Information Line (020 7649 1885)
for the latest details.

FRONT COVER *Paeonia peregrina*. Unsigned hand-coloured engraving from H. G. L. Reichenbach et al., *Icones florae Germanicae et Helveticae*,
vol. 4 (1840).

TITLE PAGE *Campanumoea lanceolata* [now *Codonopsis lanceolata*]. Unsigned hand-coloured engraving from Philipp Franz von Sieibold & J.
G. Zuccarini, *Flora Japonica* (1835–41).

OVERLEAF, LEFT *Tulipa planifolia* [now *Tulipa gesneriana*]. Hand-coloured engraving after A. Mignol from Alexis Jordan & Jules Fourreau,
Icones ad floram Europae (1866–1903).

JANUARY

M	T	W	T	F	S	S
			1	2	3	4
5	6	7	8	9	10	11
12	13	14	15	16	17	18
19	20	21	22	23	24	25
26	27	28	29	30	31	

FEBRUARY

M	T	W	T	F	S	S
						1
2	3	4	5	6	7	8
9	10	11	12	13	14	15
16	17	18	19	20	21	22
23	24	25	26	27	28	

MARCH

M	T	W	T	F	S	S
						1
2	3	4	5	6	7	8
9	10	11	12	13	14	15
16	17	18	19	20	21	22
23	24	25	26	27	28	29
30	31					

APRIL

M	T	W	T	F	S	S
		1	2	3	4	5
6	7	8	9	10	11	12
13	14	15	16	17	18	19
20	21	22	23	24	25	26
27	28	29	30			

MAY

M	T	W	T	F	S	S
				1	2	3
4	5	6	7	8	9	10
11	12	13	14	15	16	17
18	19	20	21	22	23	24
25	26	27	28	29	30	31

JUNE

M	T	W	T	F	S	S
1	2	3	4	5	6	7
8	9	10	11	12	13	14
15	16	17	18	19	20	21
22	23	24	25	26	27	28
29	30					

JULY

M	T	W	T	F	S	S
		1	2	3	4	5
6	7	8	9	10	11	12
13	14	15	16	17	18	19
20	21	22	23	24	25	26
27	28	29	30	31		

AUGUST

M	T	W	T	F	S	S
					1	2
3	4	5	6	7	8	9
10	11	12	13	14	15	16
17	18	19	20	21	22	23
24	25	26	27	28	29	30
31						

SEPTEMBER

M	T	W	T	F	S	S
	1	2	3	4	5	6
7	8	9	10	11	12	13
14	15	16	17	18	19	20
21	22	23	24	25	26	27
28	29	30				

OCTOBER

M	T	W	T	F	S	S
			1	2	3	4
5	6	7	8	9	10	11
12	13	14	15	16	17	18
19	20	21	22	23	24	25
26	27	28	29	30	31	

NOVEMBER

M	T	W	T	F	S	S
						1
2	3	4	5	6	7	8
9	10	11	12	13	14	15
16	17	18	19	20	21	22
23	24	25	26	27	28	29
30						

DECEMBER

M	T	W	T	F	S	S
	1	2	3	4	5	6
7	8	9	10	11	12	13
14	15	16	17	18	19	20
21	22	23	24	25	26	27
28	29	30	31			

JANUARY

M	T	W	T	F	S	S
				1	2	3
4	5	6	7	8	9	10
11	12	13	14	15	16	17
18	19	20	21	22	23	24
25	26	27	28	29	30	31

FEBRUARY

M	T	W	T	F	S	S
1	2	3	4	5	6	7
8	9	10	11	12	13	14
15	16	17	18	19	20	21
22	23	24	25	26	27	28

MARCH

M	T	W	T	F	S	S
1	2	3	4	5	6	7
8	9	10	11	12	13	14
15	16	17	18	19	20	21
22	23	24	25	26	27	28
29	30	31				

APRIL

M	T	W	T	F	S	S
			1	2	3	4
5	6	7	8	9	10	11
12	13	14	15	16	17	18
19	20	21	22	23	24	25
26	27	28	29	30		

MAY

M	T	W	T	F	S	S
					1	2
3	4	5	6	7	8	9
10	11	12	13	14	15	16
17	18	19	20	21	22	23
24	25	26	27	28	29	30
31						

JUNE

M	T	W	T	F	S	S
	1	2	3	4	5	6
7	8	9	10	11	12	13
14	15	16	17	18	19	20
21	22	23	24	25	26	27
28	29	30				

JULY

M	T	W	T	F	S	S
			1	2	3	4
5	6	7	8	9	10	11
12	13	14	15	16	17	18
19	20	21	22	23	24	25
26	27	28	29	30	31	

AUGUST

M	T	W	T	F	S	S
						1
2	3	4	5	6	7	8
9	10	11	12	13	14	15
16	17	18	19	20	21	22
23	24	25	26	27	28	29
30	31					

SEPTEMBER

M	T	W	T	F	S	S
		1	2	3	4	5
6	7	8	9	10	11	12
13	14	15	16	17	18	19
20	21	22	23	24	25	26
27	28	29	30			

OCTOBER

M	T	W	T	F	S	S
				1	2	3
4	5	6	7	8	9	10
11	12	13	14	15	16	17
18	19	20	21	22	23	24
25	26	27	28	29	30	31

NOVEMBER

M	T	W	T	F	S	S
1	2	3	4	5	6	7
8	9	10	11	12	13	14
15	16	17	18	19	20	21
22	23	24	25	26	27	28
29	30					

DECEMBER

M	T	W	T	F	S	S
		1	2	3	4	5
6	7	8	9	10	11	12
13	14	15	16	17	18	19
20	21	22	23	24	25	26
27	28	29	30	31		

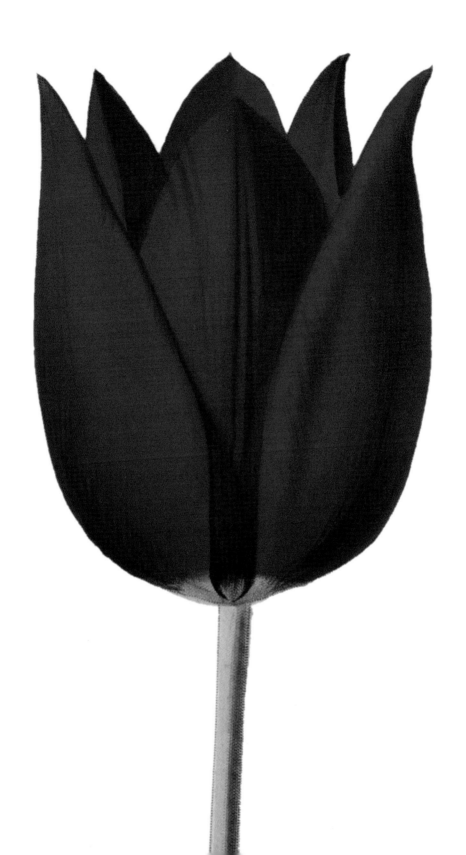

The illustrations reproduced in this diary come from four great nineteenth century multi-volume anthologies of rare and unusual plants from around the world.

The first to appear was Nathaniel Wallich's *Plantae Asiaticae Rariores*. Wallich (1786–1854) was Director of the Calcutta Botanic Garden, and his book was intended to depict the recently discovered plants not covered by previous illustrated works on the flora of India. The plates were printed by the new process of lithography, and the publication was fast, efficient, and better organized than any of its predecessors: it was published in three volumes, between 1829 and 1832, and Wallich proclaimed that it was "the cheapest of its kind published in any branch of natural history, every plate costing only two shillings". It contained 295 plant portraits based mostly on drawings by two Indian artists employed at the Garden, Gorachand and Vishnupersaud, and printed and coloured by John Clark. Only 250 copies were printed. Among the plants depicted was *Amherstia nobilis*, which Wallich named after Countess Amherst, and which was later to be introduced into England by John Gibson, the Duke of Devonshire's collector, and brought into flower at Chatsworth.

Only a few years later, Siebold and Zuccarini's *Flora Japonica* began to appear in Leiden. Philipp Franz von Siebold (1796–1866) was only the third European botanist to visit Japan, having officially gone there as an eye-doctor. He arrived in Japan in 1826, and was expelled four years later for the offence of trying to smuggle maps of Japan to Europe. But he managed to send a couple of consignments of Japanese plants to Europe, where he established a garden and nursery at Leiden, and helped to distribute Japanese plants to European gardens. (He eventually returned to Japan, after it was forcibly opened to western commerce in the 1850s.) The plates in the *Flora Japonica* were drawn by European artists, but in many cases were based on drawings by Japanese artists that Siebold had brought back, as not all the plants depicted were available in his garden. Most of the book was issued between 1835 and 1841, with 151 coloured plates, but a final portion was added in 1870, by F. A. W. Miquel, the Director of the Leiden Botanic Garden.

Meanwhile, a major work on the central European flora had been begun by Ludwig Reichenbach (1793–1869), the Director of the Dresden Botanic Garden. Reichenbach, who was a fine botanical artist, had already been issuing a miscellaneous collection of plant portraits entitled *Iconographia Botanica*; the second part of this (1837) doubled as the first volume of a new work entitled *Icones Florae Germanicae et Helveticae* – in effect, a flora of central Europe. Reichenbach was the author and illustrator for the first twelve volumes. In 1851 his son Gustav Heinrich Reichenbach (1823–89) took over the publication, and drew at least 1500 plates for the work. Gustav was a leading orchid expert and dealt with orchids in volumes 13–14; to make an already confusing publication history more tangled, he released these volumes as a separate work entitled *Tentamen Orchidographiae Europeae*. After his death, the work was continued by Beck von Mannagetta, and was finally completed in 1914 with its 25th volume.

Our final source for this diary is the *Icones ad floram Europae*, by Alexis Jordan and Jules Fourreau. This work began to appear in 1866, and was cut short in 1870 when Fourreau was killed in the Franco-Prussian War; Jordan's son Camille recommenced it in 1903, issuing the remaining plates that had already been made and supplying the residual text. The 501 coloured lithographic plates are splendid plant portraits, but the work is regarded with suspicion by botanists. Jordan (1814–97) became notorious for advocating a very narrow concept of species, and he distinguished as separate species many plants that everyone else regarded as minor variations. But in consequence these plates have a degree of careful detail that places them in the top rank of botanical illustrations.

Brent Elliott
The Royal Horticultural Society

29 Monday

30 Tuesday

31 Wednesday

New Year's Eve

1 Thursday •

New Year's Day
Holiday, UK, Republic of Ireland, Canada, USA,
Australia and New Zealand

2 Friday

Holiday, Scotland and New Zealand

3 Saturday

4 Sunday

First Quarter

Cyclamen lobospilum [now *Cyclamen repandum*]. Hand-coloured engraving after C. Delorme from Alexis Jordan & Jules Fourreau, *Icones ad floram Europae* (1866–1903).

January

5 Monday

6 Tuesday

Epiphany

7 Wednesday

8 Thursday

9 Friday

10 Saturday

11 Sunday

Full Moon

Melanorrhoea usitata. Hand-coloured engraving after Gorachand from Nathaniel Wallich, *Plantae Asiaticae rariores* (1829–32), believed to have been coloured by John Clark.

January

12 Monday

13 Tuesday

14 Wednesday

15 Thursday

16 Friday

17 Saturday

18 Sunday

Last Quarter

Amherstia nobilis. Hand-coloured engraving after Vishnupersaud from Nathaniel Wallich,
Plantae Asiaticae rariores (1829–32), believed to have been coloured by John Clark.

January

---

19 Monday

Holiday, USA (Martin Luther King's birthday)

---

20 Tuesday

---

21 Wednesday

---

22 Thursday

---

23 Friday

---

24 Saturday

---

25 Sunday

Dendrobium densiflorum. Hand-coloured engraving after Gorachand from Nathaniel Wallich,
Plantae Asiaticae rariores (1829–32), believed to have been coloured by John Clark.

26 Monday

New Moon
Chinese New Year
Holiday, Australia (Australia Day)

27 Tuesday

28 Wednesday

29 Thursday

30 Friday

31 Saturday

1 Sunday

Mussaenda macrophylla [now *Mussaenda frondosa*]. Hand-coloured engraving after Gorachand from Nathaniel Wallich, *Plantae Asiaticae rariores* (1829–32), believed to have been coloured by John Clark.

February

2 Monday

First Quarter

3 Tuesday

4 Wednesday

5 Thursday

6 Friday

Accession of Queen Elizabeth II
Holiday, New Zealand (Waitangi Day)

7 Saturday

8 Sunday

Curcuma cordata [now *Curcuma petiolata*]. Unsigned hand-coloured engraving from Nathaniel Wallich,
Plantae Asiaticae rariores (1829–32), believed to have been coloured by John Clark.

February

9 Monday

Full Moon

10 Tuesday

11 Wednesday

12 Thursday

Holiday, USA (Lincoln's Birthday)

13 Friday

14 Saturday

St. Valentine's Day

15 Sunday

Botryanthus compactus [now *Muscari botryoides*]. Unsigned hand-coloured engraving from Alexis Jordan & Jules Fourreau, *Icones ad floram Europae* (1866–1903).

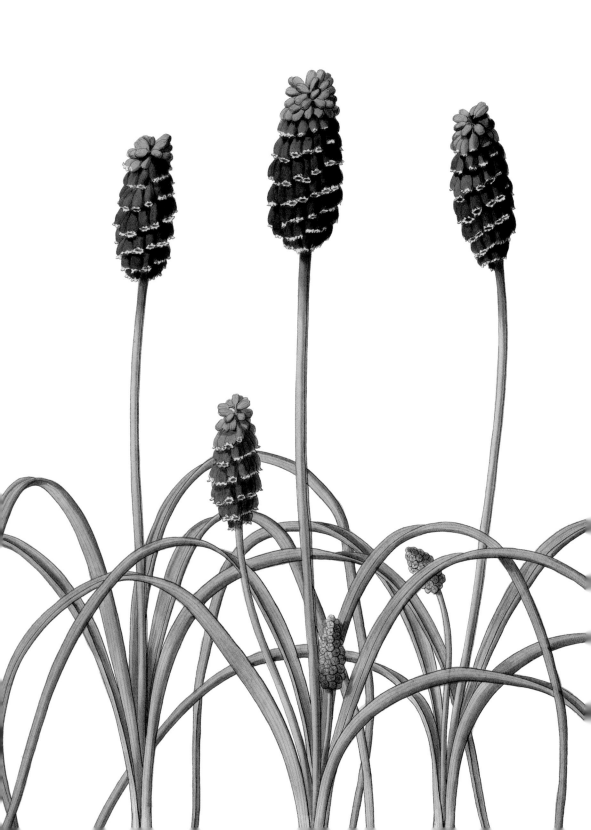

February

16 Monday

Last Quarter
Holiday, USA (Washington's Birthday)

17 Tuesday

RHS London Flower Show

18 Wednesday

RHS London Flower Show

19 Thursday

20 Friday

21 Saturday

22 Sunday

Narcissus jonquilla, Narcissus dubius, Narcissus tazetta. Unsigned hand-coloured engraving from H. G. L. Reichenbach et al., *Icones florae Germanicae et Helveticae*, vol. 9 (1847).

23 Monday

24 Tuesday

Shrove Tuesday

25 Wednesday

New Moon
Ash Wednesday

26 Thursday

27 Friday

28 Saturday

1 Sunday

St David's Day

Gentiana angustifolia. Hand-coloured engraving after H. G. Reichenbach from
H. G. L. Reichenbach et al., *Icones florae Germanicae et Helveticae*, vol. 17 (1854–55).

March

2 Monday

3 Tuesday

4 Wednesday

First Quarter

5 Thursday

6 Friday

7 Saturday

8 Sunday

Camellia japonica. Unsigned hand-coloured engraving from Philipp Franz von Siebold & J. G. Zuccarini, *Flora Japonica* (1835–41).

March

9 Monday

Commonwealth Day

10 Tuesday

11 Wednesday

Full Moon

12 Thursday

13 Friday

14 Saturday

15 Sunday

Primula x pubescens. Hand-coloured engraving after Humnitz [?] from H. G. L. Reichenbach et al.,
Icones florae Germanicae et Helveticae, vol. 17 (1854–55).

March

16 Monday

17 Tuesday

St Patrick's Day
Holiday, Northern Ireland and Republic of Ireland

18 Wednesday

Last Quarter

19 Thursday

20 Friday

Vernal Equinox

21 Saturday

RHS London Orchid Show

22 Sunday

RHS London Orchid Show
Mothering Sunday, UK

Ajax gayi [now *Narcissus pseudonarcissus cv.*, probably *N. pseudonarcissus* 'Princeps'.]. Hand-coloured engraving after C. Delorme from
Alexis Jordan & Jules Fourreau, *Icones ad floram Europae* (1866–1903).

March

23 Monday

24 Tuesday

25 Wednesday

26 Thursday

New Moon

27 Friday

28 Saturday

29 Sunday

British Summer Time begins

Aeschynanthus parviflorus. Hand-coloured engraving after Gorachand from Nathaniel Wallich, *Plantae Asiaticae rariores* (1829–32), believed to have been coloured by John Clark.

30 Monday

31 Tuesday

1 Wednesday

2 Thursday

First Quarter

3 Friday

4 Saturday

5 Sunday

Palm Sunday

Erythronium dens-canis. Unsigned hand-coloured engraving from H. G. L. Reichenbach et al., *Icones florae Germanicae et Helveticae*, vol. 10 (1848).

April

6 Monday

7 Tuesday

8 Wednesday

9 Thursday

Full Moon
Maundy Thursday
Passover (Pesach), First Day

10 Friday

Good Friday
Holiday, UK, Canada, USA, Australia and New Zealand

11 Saturday

12 Sunday

Easter Sunday

Rhododendron formosum. Hand-coloured engraving after Gorachand from Nathaniel Wallich,
Plantae Asiaticae rariores (1829–32), believed to have been coloured by John Clark.

April

---

13 Monday

Easter Monday
Holiday, UK (exc. Scotland), Republic of Ireland,
Canada, Australia and New Zealand

---

14 Tuesday

---

15 Wednesday

Passover (Pesach), Seventh Day

---

16 Thursday

Passover (Pesach), Eighth Day

---

17 Friday

Last Quarter

---

18 Saturday

---

19 Sunday

Fritillaria lutea. Unsigned hand-coloured engraving from H. G. L. Reichenbach et al.,
Icones florae Germanicae et Helveticae, vol. 10 (1848).

April

---

20 Monday

---

21 Tuesday

RHS London Flower Show
Birthday of Queen Elizabeth II

---

22 Wednesday

RHS London Flower Show

---

23 Thursday

St. George's Day

---

24 Friday

---

25 Saturday

New Moon
Holiday, Australia and New Zealand (Anzac Day)

---

26 Sunday

Magnolia insignis. Hand-coloured engraving after Vishnupersaud from Nathaniel Wallich,
Plantae Asiaticae rariores (1829–32), believed to have been coloured by John Clark.

27 Monday

28 Tuesday

29 Wednesday

30 Thursday

1 Friday

First Quarter

2 Saturday

3 Sunday

Aquilegia vulgaris. Unsigned hand-coloured engraving from H. G. L. Reichenbach et al.,
Icones florae Germanicae et Helveticae, vol. 4 (1840).

May

4 Monday

Early May Bank Holiday, UK and Republic of Ireland

5 Tuesday

6 Wednesday

7 Thursday

Malvern Spring Gardening Show

8 Friday

Malvern Spring Gardening Show

9 Saturday

Full Moon
Malvern Spring Gardening Show

10 Sunday

Mother's Day, Canada, USA, Australia and New Zealand
Malvern Spring Gardening Show

Tulipa platystigma [now *Tulipa gesneriana*]. Hand-coloured engraving after A. Mignol from Alexis Jordan & Jules Fourreau, *Icones ad floram Europae* (1866–1903).

May

11 Monday

12 Tuesday

13 Wednesday

14 Thursday

15 Friday

16 Saturday

17 Sunday

Last Quarter

Digitalis thapsi. Hand-coloured engraving after H. G. Reichenbach from H. G. L. Reichenbach et al., *Icones florae Germanicae et Helveticae*, vol. 20 (1861).

18 Monday

Holiday, Canada (Victoria Day)

19 Tuesday

Chelsea Flower Show

20 Wednesday

Chelsea Flower Show

21 Thursday

Ascension Day
Chelsea Flower Show

22 Friday

Chelsea Flower Show

23 Saturday

Chelsea Flower Show

24 Sunday

New Moon

Campanula latifolia 'Eriocarpa' [now absorbed into *Campanula latifolia*]. Hand-coloured engraving after H. G. Reichenbach from H. G. L. Reichenbach et al., *Icones florae Germanicae et Helveticae*, vol. 19 (1858–60).

25 Monday

Spring Bank Holiday, UK
Holiday, USA (Memorial Day)

26 Tuesday

27 Wednesday

28 Thursday

29 Friday

Feast of Weeks, Shavuot

30 Saturday

31 Sunday

First Quarter
Whit Sunday (Pentecost)

Iris x lurida. Hand-coloured engraving after Humnitz [?] from H. G. L. Reichenbach et al.,
Icones florae Germanicae et Helveticae, vol. 9 (1847).

1 Monday

Holiday, Republic of Ireland
Holiday, New Zealand (The Queen's birthday)

2 Tuesday

Coronation Day

3 Wednesday

4 Thursday

5 Friday

6 Saturday

7 Sunday

Full Moon
Trinity Sunday

Paeonia peregrina. Unsigned hand-coloured engraving from H. G. L. Reichenbach et al.,
Icones florae Germanicae et Helveticae, vol. 4 (1840).

June

8 Monday

9 Tuesday

10 Wednesday

Wisley Music Festival
BBC Gardeners' World Live, Birmingham

11 Thursday

Corpus Christi
Wisley Music Festival
BBC Gardeners' World Live, Birmingham

12 Friday

Wisley Music Festival
BBC Gardeners' World Live, Birmingham

13 Saturday

The Queen's official birthday (subject to confirmation)
Wisley Music Festival
BBC Gardeners' World Live, Birmingham

14 Sunday

BBC Gardeners' World Live, Birmingham

Lilium pyrenaicum. Unsigned hand-coloured engraving from H. G. L. Reichenbach et al.,
Icones florae Germanicae et Helveticae, vol. 10 (1848).

June

---

15 Monday

Last Quarter
St. Swithin's Day

---

16 Tuesday

---

17 Wednesday

---

18 Thursday

---

19 Friday

---

20 Saturday

---

21 Sunday

Summer Solstice
Father's Day, UK, Canada and USA

Identification uncertain due to lack of botanical detail shown but one of the *Delphinium* species. Unsigned hand-coloured engraving from H. G. L. Reichenbach et al., *Icones florae Germanicae et Helveticae*, vol. 4 (1840).

June

22 Monday

New Moon

23 Tuesday

24 Wednesday

25 Thursday

26 Friday

27 Saturday

28 Sunday

Althaea [Alcea] pallida, Alcea rosea. Unsigned hand-coloured engraving from H. G. L. Reichenbach et al.,
Icones florae Germanicae et Helveticae, vol. 5 (1841–42).

29 Monday

First Quarter

30 Tuesday

1 Wednesday

Holiday, Canada (Canada Day)

2 Thursday

3 Friday

Holiday, USA (Independence Day)

4 Saturday

Independence Day, USA

5 Sunday

Rosa rugosa. Hand-coloured engraving after S. Minsinger from Philipp Franz von Siebold
& J. G. Zuccarini, *Flora Japonica* (1835–41).

July

6 Monday

---

7 Tuesday

Full Moon
RHS Hampton Court Palace Flower Show

8 Wednesday

RHS Hampton Court Palace Flower Show

9 Thursday

RHS Hampton Court Palace Flower Show

10 Friday

RHS Hampton Court Palace Flower Show

11 Saturday

RHS Hampton Court Palace Flower Show

12 Sunday

RHS Hampton Court Palace Flower Show

Aconitum eminens [now *Aconitum napellus*], *Aconitum pyramidale* [now *Aconitum napellus*]. Unsigned hand-coloured engraving from H. G. L. Reichenbach et al., *Icones florae Germanicae et Helveticae*, vol. 4 (1840).

July

13 Monday

Holiday, Northern Ireland (Battle of the Boyne)

14 Tuesday

15 Wednesday

Last Quarter

16 Thursday

17 Friday

18 Saturday

19 Sunday

Hemerocallis flava [now *Hemerocallis lilioaphodelus*]. Unsigned hand-coloured engraving from H. G. L. Reichenbach et al., *Icones florae Germanicae et Helveticae*, vol. 10 (1848).

July

20 Monday

21 Tuesday

22 Wednesday

New Moon
The RHS Flower Show at Tatton Park

23 Thursday

The RHS Flower Show at Tatton Park

24 Friday

The RHS Flower Show at Tatton Park

25 Saturday

The RHS Flower Show at Tatton Park

26 Sunday

The RHS Flower Show at Tatton Park

Ligularia kaempferi [now *Farfugium japonicum*]. Hand-coloured engraving after S. Minsinger from
Philipp Franz von Siebold & J. G. Zuccarini, *Flora Japonica* (1835–41).

July & August

27 Monday

28 Tuesday

First Quarter

29 Wednesday

30 Thursday

31 Friday

1 Saturday

2 Sunday

Probably *Vinca herbacea* but identification uncertain due to lack of botanical detail shown. Hand-coloured engraving after H. G. Reichenbach from H. G. L. Reichenbach et al., *Icones florae Germanicae et Helveticae*, vol. 17 (1854–55).

August

3 Monday

Summer Bank Holiday, Scotland
Holiday, Republic of Ireland

4 Tuesday

5 Wednesday

6 Thursday

Full Moon

7 Friday

8 Saturday

9 Sunday

Nymphaea alba. Unsigned hand-coloured engraving from H. G. L. Reichenbach et al.,
Icones florae Germanicae et Helveticae, vol. 7 (1845).

August

---

10 Monday

---

11 Tuesday

---

12 Wednesday

---

13 Thursday

Last Quarter

14 Friday

---

15 Saturday

---

16 Sunday

Nerium oleander. Hand-coloured engraving after H. G. Reichenbach from H. G. L. Reichenbach et al.,
Icones florae Germanicae et Helveticae, vol. 17 (1854–55).

August

17 Monday

18 Tuesday

RHS Wisley Flower Show

19 Wednesday

RHS Wisley Flower Show

20 Thursday

New Moon
RHS Wisley Flower Show

21 Friday

22 Saturday

First Day of Ramadân (subject to sighting of the moon)

23 Sunday

Convolvulus wightii [now *Ipomoea wightii*]. Hand-coloured engraving after Vishnupersaud from Nathaniel Wallich, *Plantae Asiaticae rariores* (1829–32), believed to have been coloured by John Clark.

August

24 Monday

25 Tuesday

26 Wednesday

27 Thursday

First Quarter

28 Friday

29 Saturday

30 Sunday

Eryngium maritimum. Hand-coloured engraving after H. G. Reichenbach from H. G. L. Reichenbach et al.,
Icones florae Germanicae et Helveticae, vol. 21 (1863).

August & September

31 Monday

Summer Bank Holiday, UK exc. Scotland

1 Tuesday

2 Wednesday

3 Thursday

4 Friday

Full Moon

5 Saturday

6 Sunday

Father's Day, Australia and New Zealand

Inula hirta. Hand-coloured engraving after H. G. Reichenbach from H. G. L. Reichenbach et al.,
Icones florae Germanicae et Helveticae, vol. 16 (1853–54).

September

7 Monday

Holiday, Canada (Labour Day)
Holiday, USA (Labor Day)

8 Tuesday

9 Wednesday

10 Thursday

11 Friday

12 Saturday

Last Quarter

13 Sunday

Hibiscus hamabo. Unsigned hand-coloured engraving from Philipp Franz von Siebold
& J. G. Zuccarini, *Flora Japonica* (1835–41).

September

14 Monday

15 Tuesday

16 Wednesday

17 Thursday

18 Friday

New Moon

19 Saturday

Jewish New Year (Rosh Hashanah)

20 Sunday

Hydrangea otaksa [now *Hydrangea macrophylla* 'Otaksa']. Hand-coloured engraving after S. Minsinger from
Philipp Franz von Siebold & J. G. Zuccarini, *Flora Japonica* (1835–41).

September

21 Monday

Eid al Fitr, Ramadân ends

22 Tuesday

Autumnal Equinox

23 Wednesday

24 Thursday

25 Friday

26 Saturday

First Quarter
Malvern Autumn Show

27 Sunday

Malvern Autumn Show

Lathyrus heterophyllus. Hand-coloured engraving after Humnitz [?] from
H. G. L Reichenbach, *Icones florae Germanicae*, vol. 22 (1867).

September&October

28 Monday

Day of Atonement (Yom Kippur)

29 Tuesday

Michaelmas Day

30 Wednesday

1 Thursday

2 Friday

3 Saturday

Festival Tabernacles (Succoth), First Day

4 Sunday

Full Moon

Clematis viticella. Unsigned hand-coloured engraving from H. G. L. Reichenbach et al.,
Icones florae Germanicae et Helveticae, vol. 4 (1840).

October

5 Monday

6 Tuesday

7 Wednesday

8 Thursday

9 Friday

10 Saturday

Festival of Tabernacles (Succoth), Eighth Day

11 Sunday

Last Quarter

Eriophorum scheuchzeri. Unsigned hand-coloured engraving from H. G. L. Reichenbach et al., *Icones florae Germanicae et Helveticae*, vol. 8 (1846).

October

---

12 Monday

Holiday, Canada, (Thanksgiving Day)
Holiday, USA (Columbus Day)

---

13 Tuesday

RHS London Autumn Show

---

14 Wednesday

RHS London Autumn Show

---

15 Thursday

---

16 Friday

---

17 Saturday

---

18 Sunday

New Moon

Hydrangea azisai [now *Hydrangea macrophylla* 'Azisai']. Hand-coloured engraving after H. Popp from
Philipp Franz von Siebold & J. G. Zuccarini, *Flora Japonica* (1835–41).

October

19 Monday

20 Tuesday

21 Wednesday

22 Thursday

23 Friday

24 Saturday

United Nations Day

25 Sunday

British Summer Time ends

Aria ellipsoidea [now *Sorbus aria*]. Hand-coloured engraving after C. Delorme from Alexis Jordan & Jules Fourreau, *Icones ad floram Europae* (1866–1903).

October&November

26 Monday

First Quarter
Holiday, Republic of Ireland
Holiday, New Zealand (Labour Day)

27 Tuesday

28 Wednesday

29 Thursday

30 Friday

31 Saturday

Hallowe'en

1 Sunday

All Saints' Day

Crinum zeylanicum. Hand-coloured engraving after Vishnupersaud from Nathaniel Wallich,
Plantae Asiaticae rariores (1829–32), believed to have been coloured by John Clark.

November

2 Monday

Full Moon

3 Tuesday

4 Wednesday

5 Thursday

Guy Fawkes' Day

6 Friday

7 Saturday

8 Sunday

Remembrance Sunday, UK

Leycesteria formosa. Hand-coloured engraving after Gorachand from Nathaniel Wallich,
Plantae Asiaticae rariores (1829–32), believed to have been coloured by John Clark.

November

9 Monday

Last Quarter

10 Tuesday

11 Wednesday

Holiday, Canada (Remembrance Day)
Holiday, USA (Veterans Day)

12 Thursday

13 Friday

14 Saturday

15 Sunday

Osbeckia angustifolia [now *Osbeckia chinensis* var. *angustifolia*]. Hand-coloured engraving after Gorachand from Nathaniel Wallich, *Plantae Asiaticae rariores* (1829–32), believed to have been coloured by John Clark.

November

16 Monday

New Moon

17 Tuesday

18 Wednesday

19 Thursday

20 Friday

21 Saturday

22 Sunday

Meyenia hawtayneana. Hand-coloured engraving after Gorachand from Nathaniel Wallich,
Plantae Asiaticae rariores (1829–32), believed to have been coloured by John Clark.

November

23 Monday

24 Tuesday

First Quarter

25 Wednesday

26 Thursday

Holiday, USA (Thanksgiving Day)

27 Friday

28 Saturday

29 Sunday

First Sunday in Advent

Fortunella japonica. Hand-coloured engraving after H. Popp from Philipp Franz von Siebold
& J. G. Zuccarini, *Flora Japonica* (1835–41).

November&December

30 Monday

St Andrew's Day

1 Tuesday

2 Wednesday

Full Moon

3 Thursday

4 Friday

5 Saturday

6 Sunday

Corylus avellana. Unsigned hand-coloured engraving from H. G. L. Reichenbach et al.,
Icones florae Germanicae et Helveticae, vol. 12 (1850).

December

---

7 Monday

---

8 Tuesday

---

9 Wednesday

Last Quarter

---

10 Thursday

---

11 Friday

---

12 Saturday

Jewish Festival of Chanukah, First Day

---

13 Sunday

Physalis alkekengi. Hand-coloured engraving after H. G. Reichenbach from H. G. L. Reichenbach et al.,
Icones florae Germanicae et Helveticae, vol. 20 (1861).

December

14 Monday

15 Tuesday

16 Wednesday

New Moon

17 Thursday

18 Friday

Islamic New Year (subject to sighting of the moon)

19 Saturday

20 Sunday

Viscum album. Hand-coloured engraving after F. G. Kohl from H. G. L. Reichenbach et al.,
Icones florae Germanicae et Helveticae, vol. 24 (1908).

December

---

21 Monday

Winter Solstice

---

22 Tuesday

---

23 Wednesday

---

24 Thursday

First Quarter
Christmas Eve

---

25 Friday

Christmas Day
Holiday, UK, Republic of Ireland, Canada,
USA, Australia and New Zealand

---

26 Saturday

Boxing Day (St. Stephen's Day)

---

27 Sunday

Larix europaea [now *Larix decidua*]. Unsigned hand-coloured engraving from H. G. L. Reichenbach et al.,
Icones florae Germanicae et Helveticae, vol. 11 (1849).

December & January

28 Monday

Holiday, UK and Canada

29 Tuesday

30 Wednesday

31 Thursday

Full Moon
New Year's Eve

1 Friday

New Year's Day
Holiday, UK, Republic of Ireland, Canada,
USA, Australia and New Zealand

2 Saturday

Holiday, Scotland and New Zealand

3 Sunday

Myristica amygdalina [now *Horsfieldia amygdalina*]. Hand-coloured engraving after Vishnupersaud from Nathaniel Wallich, *Plantae Asiaticae rariores* (1829–32), believed to have been coloured by John Clark.

AUSTRIA	JAN 1, 6; APR 12, 13; MAY 1, 21, 31; JUN 1, 11; AUG 15; OCT 26; NOV 1; DEC 8, 25, 26
BELGIUM	JAN 1; APR 12, 13; MAY 1, 21, 31; JUN 1; JUL 11, 21; AUG 15; SEP 27; NOV 1, 11, 15; DEC 25
BULGARIA	JAN 1; MAR 3; APR 19, 20; MAY 1, 6, 24; SEP 6, 21, 22; NOV 1; DEC 24, 25, 26
CROATIA	JAN 1, 6; APR 10, 12, 13; MAY 1; JUN 11, 22, 25; AUG 5, 15; OCT 8; NOV 1; DEC 25, 26
CYPRUS	JAN 1, 6; MAR 2, 25; APR 1, 17, 19, 20; MAY 1; JUN 7, 8; AUG 15; OCT 1, 28; DEC 25, 26
CZECH REPUBLIC	JAN 1; APR 12, 13; MAY 1, 8; JUL 5, 6; SEP 28; OCT 28; NOV 17; DEC 24, 25, 26
DENMARK	JAN 1; APR 9, 10, 12, 13; MAY 8, 21, 31; JUN 1, 5; DEC 25, 26
ESTONIA	JAN 1; FEB 24; APR 10, 12; MAY 1, 31; JUN 23, 24; AUG 20; DEC 24, 25, 26
FINLAND	JAN 1, 6; APR 10, 12, 13; MAY 1, 21, 31; JUN 20; OCT 31; DEC 6, 25, 26
FRANCE	JAN 1; APR 10, 12, 13; MAY 1, 8, 21, 31; JUN 1; JUL 14; AUG 15; NOV 1, 11; DEC 25
GERMANY	JAN 1, 6; APR 10, 12, 13; MAY 1, 21, 31; JUN 1, 11; AUG 15; OCT 3, 31; NOV 1, 18; DEC 25, 26
GREECE	JAN 1, 6; MAR 2, 25; APR 17, 19, 20; MAY 1; JUN 7, 8; AUG 15; OCT 28; DEC 25, 26
HUNGARY	JAN 1; MAR 15; APR 12, 13; MAY 1, 31; JUN 1; AUG 20, 21; OCT 23; NOV 1; DEC 25, 26
ITALY	JAN 1, 6; APR 12, 13; 25; MAY 1; JUN 2; AUG 15; NOV 1; DEC 8, 25, 26
LATVIA	JAN 1; APR 10, 12, 13; MAY 1, 4; JUN 22, 23, 24; NOV 18; DEC 25, 26, 31
LITHUANIA	JAN 1; FEB 16; MAR 11; APR 12, 13, 14; MAY 1, 3, 4; JUN 24; JUL 6; AUG 15,17; NOV 1, 2; DEC 25, 26, 28
LUXEMBOURG	JAN 1; FEB 23; APR 12, 13; MAY 1, 21, 31; JUN 1, 23; AUG 15; SEP 7; NOV 1; DEC 25, 26
MALTA	JAN 1; FEB 10; MAR 19, 31; APR 10, 12; MAY 1; JUN 7, 29; AUG 15; SEP 8, 21; DEC 8, 13, 25
NETHERLANDS	JAN 1; APR 10, 12, 13, 30; MAY 21, 31; JUN 1; DEC 25, 26
NORWAY	JAN 1; APR 9, 10, 12, 13; MAY 1, 17, 21, 31; JUN 1; DEC 25, 26
POLAND	JAN 1; APR 12, 13; MAY 1, 3; JUN 11; AUG 15; NOV 1, 11; DEC 25, 26
PORTUGAL	JAN 1; FEB 24; APR 10, 12, 13, 25; MAY 1; JUN 10, 11, 13; AUG 15; OCT 5; NOV 1; DEC 1, 8, 25
ROMANIA	JAN 1, 2; APR 19, 20; MAY 1; DEC 1, 25, 26
SLOVAKIA	JAN 1, 6; APR 10, 12, 13; MAY 1, 8; JUL 5; AUG 29; SEP 1, 15; NOV 1, 17; DEC 24, 25, 26
SLOVENIA	JAN 1, 2; FEB 8; APR 12, 13, 27; MAY 1, 2, 31; JUN 25; AUG 15; OCT 31; NOV 1; DEC 25, 26
SPAIN	JAN 1, 6; APR 9, 10, 12, 13; MAY 1, 31; AUG 15; OCT 12; NOV 1, 9; DEC 6, 8, 25, 26
SWEDEN	JAN 1, 6; APR 10, 12, 13; MAY 1, 21, 31; JUN 6, 20; OCT 31; DEC 25, 26
SWITZERLAND	JAN 1, 2; APR 10, 12, 13; MAY 1, 21, 31; JUN 1; AUG 1, 15; NOV 1; DEC 8, 25, 26